no count
COOKBOOK

weight watchers

Eating healthier makes life better. *And it tastes amazing.*

no count
COOKBOOK

weight
watchers

The recipes

● The recipes in this book use foods from the No Count Food List and the flavour boosters list. Some of the cook's tips may suggest using foods that are not included on either of these lists – if this is the case, we have pointed out that you may need to use some of your weekly SmartPoints allowance if you want to use these in the recipe.

● All the recipe ingredients have quantities listed, however if you are following the No Count approach, you need only use these as a guide as there is no need to weigh or measure anything.

● If you're counting, we have included SmartPoints values for each recipe, as well as each serving per recipe. You'll also find a SmartPoints values index on page 130. This tells you how many SmartPoints values per serving each recipe contains, in order of low to high, to make it easy to search.

The small print

EGGS
Recipes use medium eggs, unless otherwise stated. Pregnant women, the elderly and children should avoid recipes with eggs which are raw or not fully cooked.

LOW-FAT SPREAD
When a recipe uses a low-fat spread, we mean a spread with a fat content of no less than 38%.

MICROWAVES
If we have used a microwave in any of our recipes, the timings will be for an 850-watt microwave oven.

PREP AND COOKING TIMES
These are approximate and meant to be guidelines. Prep time includes all the steps up to and following the main cooking time(s).

LOW FAT SOFT CHEESE
Where a recipe uses low fat soft cheese, we mean a soft cheese with a fat content of no less than 5%.

WHEN YOU SEE THESE SYMBOLS:

 Tells you how many SmartPoints are in the recipe.

❋ Indicates a recipe that is suitable for freezing.

GF Indicates a recipe that is gluten free or can be made gluten free with a few simple swaps, for example by using gluten free soy sauce.

V Indicates a recipe that is vegetarian.

Seven.

Produced by Seven Publishing on behalf of Weight Watchers International, Inc. Published March 2016. All rights reserved. No part of this publication may be reproduced, stored in a retrieval system or transmitted in any form by any means, electronic, mechanical photocopying, recording or otherwise, without the prior written permission of Seven Publishing.

First published in Great Britain by Seven Publishing Ltd.
Copyright © 2016, Weight Watchers International, Inc.

Seven Publishing Ltd
3-7 Herbal Hill
London
EC1R 5EJ
www.seven.co.uk

This book is copyright under the Berne Convention. No reproduction without permission. All rights reserved.

10 9 8 7 6 5 4 3 2

Weight Watchers SmartPoints and the SmartPoints icon are the registered trademarks of Weight Watchers International, Inc and are used under license by Weight Watchers (UK) Ltd. All rights reserved.

A CIP catalogue record for this book is available from the British Library.
ISBN: 978-0-9935835-0-6

WEIGHT WATCHERS PUBLICATIONS TEAM
Imogen Prescott, Samantha Rees, Stephanie Williams, Danielle Smith, Nicola Kirk.
Special thanks to Weight Watchers Australasia.

FOR SEVEN PUBLISHING LTD
FOOD
Food editor: Sarah Akhurst
Food assistants: Linzi Brechin, Nadine Brown, Gabrielle English

EDITORIAL
Editor-in-Chief Helen Renshaw
Editor Ward Hellewell

DESIGN & PHOTOGRAPHY
Art director Liz Baird
Photography Alex Luck
Food stylists Sarah Cook, Catherine Hill, assisted by Imogen Rose
Prop stylist Luis Peral **Prop stylist (cover)** Linda Berlin
Picture editor Carl Palmer

ACCOUNT MANAGEMENT
Account manager Jo Brennan
Business Director, retail Andy Roughton
Group publishing director Kirsten Price

PRODUCTION
Production director Sophie Dillon
Colour reproduction by F1 Colour **Printed in Italy** by L.E.G.O S.p.A

Contents

Losing weight the No Count way

couldn't be simpler and the good news is you can do it while enjoying mouthwatering meals you've made yourself. All you have to do is stick to the list of No Count foods and flavour boosters. There's **no measuring, no tracking**, and you don't have to worry about portion sizes – you just eat until you feel satisfied. And because the list includes a wide variety of foods from every food group – fruit, vegetables, meat, fish, grains and more – making **delicious, filling meals is easy**.

This book contains more than 60 recipes to give you just a taste of what's possible with No Count. From breezy **breakfasts** to stress-free **evening meals**, cooking to impress guests and **vegetarian** favourites, quick **snacks** and surprisingly simple **desserts**, these are recipes you'll want to return to again and again.

If you are counting SmartPoints, don't worry – you can still enjoy all the recipes in this book. Each one includes the SmartPoints values per serving and for the whole recipe, plus we've included a SmartPoints values index of all the recipes on page 130 to make them easy to find.

Cooking your own meals from scratch the No Count way means you'll know exactly what has gone into them, and even if you're not quite a whizz in the kitchen (yet), you'll find the recipes in this book **quick and easy** to follow and simple to achieve. We hope you'll enjoy making them, and that they will inspire you to come up with your own ideas using the ingredients on the No Count Food List which you will find on page 10.

The No Count Food List

You can use any of these ingredients in your No Count recipes…

BAKERY
- Calorie controlled brown bread
- Crumpets

CEREALS
- Oat bran
- Porridge oats
- Puffed wheat (no added sugar or salt)
- Wheat Bran, dried
- Wheatgerm, dried
- Wholegrain wheat cereal (Shredded Wheat)

COOKING INGREDIENTS
- Garlic
- Ginger, fresh
- Herbs, fresh

CRISPS, SAVOURY SNACKS & NUTS
- Popcorn, plain (no added oil or flavours)

DAIRY & EGGS
- 0% fat natural Greek yogurt
- Cottage cheese, reduced fat, natural
- Duck egg
- Egg white
- Egg, whole
- Fat free natural fromage frais
- Fat free natural yogurt
- Fromage frais, natural
- Goose egg
- Quail egg

Remember…

With the No Count approach, you can also have 2 tsp healthy oil per day (olive, sunflower, safflower, rapeseed or flaxseed).

- Quark
- Skimmed milk
- Soya yogurt, plain
- UHT skimmed milk
- Unsweetened soya milk
- Yogurt, low fat natural

FISH, MEAT & POULTRY
- Anchovies (not in oil)
- Bacon medallions
- Beef mince, extra lean (5% fat)
- Bison fillet steak, lean
- Braising steak, lean
- Bream, red or black
- Buffalo
- Chicken breast, skinless
- Chicken drumstick, skinless
- Chicken leg, skinless
- Chicken mince
- Chicken, roast, light meat, skinless
- Clams
- Cockles
- Cod
- Coley
- Crab
- Crayfish
- Dover sole
- Fillet steak, lean
- Frogs legs
- Gammon steak
- Goat
- Grey mullet
- Grouper
- Guinea fowl
- Haddock
- Hake

- Halibut
- Ham
- Heart
- Hoki
- John Dory
- Kangaroo steak
- Kidney: lamb, pig
- King prawns
- Lemon sole
- Liver
- Lobster
- Monkfish
- Mussels
- Octopus
- Orange roughy
- Ostrich
- Oysters
- Partridge
- Pigeon
- Pike
- Plaice
- Pollock
- Pork escalope
- Pork fillet
- Pork leg joint, lean
- Pork loin steak, lean
- Pork mince, extra lean (5% fat)
- Pork shoulder joint, lean
- Pork tenderloin
- Prawns
- Quail
- Rabbit
- Rainbow trout
- Red mullet
- Red snapper (Red sea bream)
- Rock salmon (Dog fish)
- Roe
- Rump steak, lean
- Salmon

- Salmon, pink or red, canned
- Sardines, fresh
- Scallops
- Sea bass
- Sea bream
- Seafood selection
- Seafood sticks
- Shark
- Shrimps
- Silverside, lean
- Sirloin steak, lean
- Skate
- Smoked cod
- Smoked haddock
- Smoked trout
- Snails
- Sprats
- Squid
- Stewing steak, lean
- Swordfish
- Tiger prawns
- Tilapia
- Tripe
- Trout
- Tuna in brine, drained
- Tuna in spring water, drained
- Tuna, raw
- Turbot
- Turkey breast fillet
- Turkey breast mince
- Turkey breast, skinless
- Turkey rasher
- Turkey steak
- Turkey thigh
- Turkey, roast, skinless
- Turkey, wafer thin
- Veal escalope
- Venison

- Wafer thin chicken
- Whelks
- Whiting
- Wild boar
- Winkles, cooked

FRUIT & VEGETABLES
- Fresh (except avocado)
- Frozen
- Tinned in natural juice or water, drained

TINS, PACKETS & JARS
- Aduki beans
- Amaranth grain
- Baked beans
- Black eyed beans
- Borlotti beans
- Broad beans
- Brown basmati rice
- Brown rice
- Buckwheat
- Bulgur wheat
- Butter beans
- Cannellini beans
- Chick peas
- Flageolet beans
- Freekeh
- French beans
- Haricot beans
- Kidney beans
- Lentils
- Millet
- Mixed beans
- Mung beans

- Pickled beetroot
- Pickled gherkins
- Pickled onions
- Pinto beans
- Quinoa
- Soya beans
- Spelt
- Sugar free jelly crystals
- Sugar free jelly, ready to eat
- Wholewheat couscous
- Wholewheat pasta
- Wild rice
- Yellow split peas

VEGETARIAN FOODS
- Quorn fillet
- Quorn mince
- Quorn pieces
- Soya mince
- Tofu, plain
- Tofu, smoked

WEIGHT WATCHERS PRODUCTS
- Extra trimmed Unsmoked Back Bacon
- Love Fibre Pitta Breads
- Love Fibre Wraps
- Petits Pains
- Quark
- Sliced Brown Bread
- Sliced Brown Danish Bread
- Tortilla Wraps

Flavour Boosters
Use these ingredients in the quantities specified, for zero SmartPoints. If no quantity is specified, you can use as much as you like.

- **Capers, 1 tsp**
- **Chilli (fresh, dried or flakes)**
- **Fat-free tomato salsa, 1 tsp**
- **Fish sauce (Nam Pla), 1 tbsp**
- **Garlic**
- **Ginger**
- **Harissa paste, 1 tsp**
- **Herbs & spices (fresh or dried)**
- **Hot pepper sauce (Tabasco), 1 tsp**
- **Lemongrass**
- **Lemon or lime juice**
- **Mustard (any), 1 tsp**
- **Soy sauce, 1 tsp**
- **Tomato purée, 1 tsp**
- **Unsweetened pickled veg, 1 tbsp**
- **Vanilla extract, 1 tsp**
- **Vinegar**
- **Worcestershire sauce, 1 tsp**
- **Yeast extract (Marmite), 1 tsp**
- **Zest of lemon, lime or orange, 1 tsp**

Smart shopping

Creating delicious healthy No Count meals is all about the ingredients, and that starts with your shopping trip. Here are some ways to avoid the pitfalls of supermarket shopping and come home with just what you need.

1 PLAN AHEAD
Work out a weekly meal plan and you won't be stuck thinking about what to eat every night. If you only shop once a week, plan to use ingredients that spoil quickly earlier in the week.

2 SNACK TIME
As well as your main meals, think about snacks for the week, too. Buy extra carrots, celery, cucumber and peppers and you'll always have something crunchy, tasty and fresh whenever you fancy it.

3 KEEP IT CLEAN
Clean out your fridge and cupboards regularly – that way you'll know exactly what you've already got on hand and what you need to buy.

4 MAKE A LIST
Whether you're shopping online or in store, make a list of all the ingredients you'll need, as well as the quantities. When you stick to a shopping list, not only will you remember everything, you won't buy things you don't need.

5 GET IN THE MOOD
Don't shop when you're feeling hungry or stressed – if you do, you'll be more likely to give into temptation. If possible, stay focused and don't go shopping with the kids!

6 CHOOSE THE RIGHT PACK SIZES
Don't buy a 2kg bag of potatoes if you only need 500g. This helps you avoid both waste, and the temptation to make (and eat) bigger portions, unless you're planning on batch cooking.

7 READ THE LABELS
You need to know exactly what you're buying, so make sure the canned fruit you've chosen is in juice, not syrup, and your mince is 5% fat, not 20%. Check labels of canned or packaged goods, such as breakfast cereals, for hidden sugar, salt or fat. As a rule, the fewer ingredients in the product, the better.

8 PAY FOR CONVENIENCE
Ready-prepared fruit and vegetables can be more expensive, but they're also great time savers. If you lead a busy life, you'll be more likely to eat fruit or veg if it's already prepared, so it may be worth spending that little bit more.

9 DOWNSIZE YOUR TROLLEY
Shop in store with a small trolley or even a hand basket – that way you will be less tempted to put any extra items in there.

10 NO-GO AREAS
Don't venture into the junk food aisles. In most supermarkets, the fresh produce is around the edges of the store.

Fresh, frozen or tinned?

Fruit and vegetables are such an important part of the No Count approach, but is fresh always best, or are frozen and tinned just as good? Here's a guide to the pros and cons.

Fresh
PROS
- Fresh vegetables have lots of natural flavour, colour and crispness. For dishes like salads and stir fries, fresh is often the best choice.
- Some veg, especially those with a high water content, such as cabbage, and salad vegetables like lettuces, cucumbers, celery and peppers, don't freeze well, so fresh is really the only option.

CONS
- Will start to lose nutrients from the moment they're picked, so buy them as fresh as possible and use as soon as you can – if possible, buy them from local producers and when in season, so you know they haven't spent ages in transit to the store.
- Can be more time consuming and fiddly to prepare.

GREAT FRESH BUYS
Salad and leaf vegetables, broccoli, cauliflower, asparagus, sprouts, citrus fruits.

Frozen
PROS
- Very convenient – frozen vegetables are easy to use as they're usually peeled and chopped for you.
- Properly stored, they'll last for ages, so you can always have them to hand.
- Freezing helps to preserve the vegetables' nutrients, so they can be just as good as, if not better than, fresh.
- Can be cheaper than fresh.

CONS
- Freezing can alter the texture, so frozen vegetables are best used for cooking as side dishes, or in soups, stews and casseroles. It all depends how you want to use it – frozen spinach, for example is great for a frittata, but not so good for salads!
- Freezing can also affect the flavour of vegetables.

GREAT FROZEN BUYS
Peas, spinach, sweetcorn, broad beans, berries.

Tinned
PROS
- Convenient – other than opening the tin, there's hardly any preparation needed.
- Easy to store – you can keep them for ages in the storecupboard, so they're great for last-minute meals.
- Lots of variety – if you're finding it difficult to get something fresh out of season, you can usually find it in a tin.
- As with freezing, the canning process helps preserve the nutrients.

CONS
- Tinned fruit and veg are generally heated before canning, which may dramatically alter their texture, flavour and colour.
- Can be high in salt and may contain added sugar! Check the label and, if necessary, drain and rinse veg such as beans or lentils before using. Only buy fruit in natural juice and drain before using.

GREAT TINNED BUYS
Tomatoes, sweetcorn, artichokes, beans, beetroot, cherries.

Batch cooking, freezing & getting ahead

With just a little extra effort you can double your reward in the kitchen by cooking double the amount, then freezing half for chilling or freezing. Batch cooking saves energy, money and time later on – especially handy for those mid-week meals.

With a little forward planning, you can plan a whole week's menu and cook elements of it all in one go. For example, if you're planning to make a dish that uses pulses or grains, cook twice what you need. That way you can have a stash of ready-to-use healthy carbs in the fridge, which makes the perfect base for another dish later in the week. They can be stored in air-tight containers for up to three days.

Sauces and vegetables can also be batch-cooked in advance, then used in other meals during the week. If you can set aside some time in the kitchen on the weekend, you'll be patting yourself on the back by Friday when you realise how easy you've made your life. Try some of these simple cook-ahead ideas:

Roasted veg

Roughly cubed aubergines, peppers, courgettes and onions can be batch-roasted, cooled, bagged and chilled for use throughout the week. They're perfect teamed with chicken, fish and pulses. The roasted butternut squash and red onions on page 65 not only work well with pasta, they're also great stirred through a risotto or teamed with couscous and brown rice for a flavour-packed lunch.

Bean salads

The black bean salad on page 40 is a fantastically vibrant dish that is not only put together in minutes, but is also endlessly versatile. It'll keep in the fridge for a few days, so make double and

enjoy it on its own for lunch, then try teaming it with Cajun spiced prawns, roast chicken or grilled fish for dinner later in the week.

Classic tomato sauces

A good tomato sauce can form the basis of so many fantastic meals. Check out the spicy tomato sauce on page 96 and cook up a couple of batches, then get creative. Flavour it with smoked paprika and add canned black beans, mince and fresh coriander for a simple chilli. Add a little rosemary and spoon over chicken thighs before roasting, or mix the sauce with roasted peppers and stir in chunks of firm fleshed fish for a super-quick fish stew.

Beef ragù

A simple beef mince and tomato sauce is a real crowd pleaser and a great freezable recipe that you can use in so many ways. We added some Indian-style flavours to make the keema pies on page 48 – you could leave out the spices (or add your favourite ones) then layer the sauce with slices of griddled aubergines and top with fat-free yogurt combined with eggs and herbs for a delicious moussaka. Or, even easier, team it with wholewheat spaghetti for the perfect Bolognese.

Easy freezy

Most soups, stews and slow-cook dishes can be frozen (without garnishes), so they're ideal for batch cooking. Store them in single-portion sizes so you can defrost just what you need. When freezing food, allow it to cool first, then immediately transfer to zip-lock freezer bags or sealable, plastic containers. Label them with the name of the dish and the date it was cooked, then put in the freezer until needed. Properly frozen, most foods can stay in the freezer for several months, but it's best to use it sooner than this, as frozen food can lose flavour over time.

Breakfast, lunch & brunch

Plus

3 ways with porridge

How to transform your breakfast bowl of oats into something special. Page 34

Scrambled eggs with mushrooms & smoked trout

This is a great way to make simple scrambled eggs so much more special. The trout gives the dish a delicious smoky flavour.

SERVES 2

PREP TIME
5 minutes

COOK TIME
10 minutes

4 large flat mushrooms
Calorie controlled cooking spray
4 eggs
2 tablespoons chopped
fresh chives
1 large garlic clove, crushed

4 tablespoons skimmed milk
125g hot-smoked trout, flaked
into large pieces
Few sprigs fresh dill
½ lemon, cut into wedges
Freshly ground black pepper

1   Heat the grill to medium-high and line a grill pan with foil. Lightly mist the mushrooms with cooking spray on both sides and put them, stalk-side down, on the grill pan. Cook under the grill for 6 minutes, then turn, season and cook for a further 3-4 minutes.

2   Meanwhile, whisk the eggs, chives, garlic and milk together, and season. Mist a nonstick frying pan with cooking spray and heat over a medium heat. Add the egg mixture and cook, stirring slowly for 2-3 minutes or until cooked to your liking.

3   Divide the mushrooms between 2 plates, top with the egg, then scatter the smoked trout over. Season to taste and serve with dill and lemon wedges.

IF YOU'RE COUNTING

SmartPoints values per serving 6
SmartPoints values per recipe 12

Top tip...

Instead of trout, try using Weight Watchers bacon medallions for 5 SmartPoints values per serving.

Quick shakshuka

This dish of eggs poached in a pepper, aubergine and tomato stew originated in north Africa, where it's often eaten for breakfast.

SERVES 1

PREP TIME
5 minutes

COOK TIME
10 minutes

Calorie controlled cooking spray
¼ red pepper, deseeded and chopped
½ small aubergine, diced
½ teaspoon ground cumin
230g tin chopped tomatoes

2 eggs
Small handful of fresh coriander
1 tablespoon 0% fat natural Greek yogurt
Freshly ground black pepper

1 Mist a small nonstick frying pan with cooking spay. Add the pepper and aubergine, and cook over a medium heat, covered, stirring occasionally, for 2-3 minutes until the vegetables are softened. If they start to stick, add a little water.

2 Stir in the ground cumin and tomatoes, and bring to a simmer.

3 Use a spoon to make 2 dips in the sauce, then break an egg into each one. Cover and simmer until the eggs are cooked to your liking – it will take 4-5 minutes for partly runny yolks.

4 Season to taste and top with the coriander leaves and yogurt to serve.

IF YOU'RE COUNTING
SmartPoints values per serving 5
SmartPoints values per recipe 5

Breakfast wrap

Everything you love in a cooked breakfast, all conveniently rolled up in a simple wrap – this is a great way to start a busy day.

SERVES 1

PREP TIME
15 minutes

COOK TIME
10 minutes

Calorie controlled cooking spray
2 slices Weight Watchers Extra Trimmed Unsmoked Back Bacon
5 cherry tomatoes, halved

1 egg
1 tablespoon skimmed milk
1 Weight Watchers Tortilla Wrap
30g baby spinach leaves

1   Mist a frying pan with cooking spray and put over a medium heat. Add the bacon and tomatoes, and cook for 3-4 minutes on each side until the bacon is golden brown and the tomatoes have softened.

2   In a small bowl, beat the egg with the skimmed milk. Pour into a small saucepan and cook over a medium heat, stirring, until set.

3   Warm the wrap in a dry frying pan over a medium heat for about 30 seconds on each side, or microwave it for 20 seconds. Put it on a plate and top with the bacon and tomatoes.

4   Spoon the scrambled egg into the middle of the wrap. Top with the spinach leaves and fold in half to serve.

IF YOU'RE COUNTING
SmartPoints values per serving 6
SmartPoints values per recipe 6

Salmon, asparagus & lentil salad

Keep some dried lentils and tinned salmon in your storecupboard for this single-serve salad that's really simple to put together.

SERVES 1

PREP TIME
10 minutes

COOK TIME
20 minutes

40g dried Puy lentils
30g frozen peas
100g asparagus,
sliced diagonally
½ celery stick, finely chopped
15g watercress
2 teaspoons chopped,
fresh dill

100g tinned red salmon,
drained and flaked

FOR THE DRESSING
2 tablespoons 0% fat natural
Greek yogurt
1 teaspoon wholegrain mustard
Squeeze of lemon juice

1   Bring a pan of water to the boil and cook the lentils for 20 minutes, or until tender. Add the peas and asparagus for the last 5 minutes.

2   Drain well and stir through the chopped celery, watercress and dill. Mix in the salmon.

3   Whisk together all the dressing ingredients in a small bowl, and drizzle over the salad to serve.

IF YOU'RE COUNTING
SmartPoints values per serving 8
SmartPoints values per recipe 8

Top tip...

Save time by using tinned lentils instead of dried. Store leftover lentils in a sealed container in the fridge.

Chicken, borlotti bean & vegetable soup with pistou

Pistou is a French version of Italian pesto, but without the pine nuts. This recipe uses parsley and mint instead of the usual basil.

SERVES 4

PREP TIME
15 minutes

COOK TIME
55 minutes

Small handful of fresh flat-leaf parsley, roughly chopped
Small handful of fresh mint leaves, roughly chopped
Grated zest of ½ a lemon
2 garlic cloves, crushed
Calorie controlled cooking spray
1 small leek, thinly sliced
2 skinless chicken breasts

1.5 litres chicken stock, made with 1 stock cube (ensure gluten free)
100g broccoli, cut into florets
200g asparagus, trimmed and chopped
120g frozen peas
400g tin borlotti beans, drained
100g sugar snap peas, sliced

1   Make the pistou. Put the parsley, mint, lemon zest and half the garlic in a food processor with 1 teaspoon water and process until smooth.

2   Mist a large saucepan with cooking spray, then put over a medium heat. Add the leek and the remaining garlic, and cook, stirring, for 5 minutes or until softened.

3   Add the whole chicken breasts and the stock to the pan with the leek, and simmer, covered, for 15 minutes or until the chicken is cooked through. Transfer the chicken to a board with a slotted spoon. Set aside to rest for 5 minutes, then slice thinly.

4   Add the broccoli, asparagus, peas and borlotti beans to the soup and bring to the boil. Reduce the heat and simmer, uncovered, for 3 minutes. Add the sugar snaps and sliced chicken, and simmer, uncovered, for 2 minutes or until the vegetables are just tender. Serve the soup topped with the pistou.

IF YOU'RE COUNTING
SmartPoints values per serving 3
SmartPoints values per recipe 11

Parsnip, apple & butternut squash soup

A velvety smooth soup that has a lovely natural sweetness from the apple and vegetables. The quark adds a delicious creaminess.

SERVES 4

PREP TIME
15 minutes

COOK TIME
35 minutes

Calorie controlled cooking spray
1 onion, chopped
1 tablespoon curry powder
700g butternut squash, peeled and cubed
300g parsnips, chopped
1 green apple, peeled, cored and chopped

1 litre vegetable stock, made with 1 stock cube (ensure gluten free)
4 tablespoons quark
1 tablespoon chopped fresh sage
Freshly ground black pepper

1 Mist a large saucepan with the cooking spray and put over a medium heat. Cook the onion for 5 minutes or until softened. Add the curry powder and cook for 30 seconds or until fragrant.

2 Add the butternut squash, parsnips, apple and stock. Bring to the boil, then reduce the heat and simmer, covered, for 20 minutes or until the vegetables are soft.

3 Using a stick blender or food processor, process the soup until smooth. Season to taste, then return the soup to the pan, put over a medium heat and cook, stirring, for 2-3 minutes or until heated through. Serve topped with a dollop of quark and sprinkled with sage.

IF YOU'RE COUNTING
SmartPoints values per serving 4
SmartPoints values per recipe 14

Top tip...
For a more intense flavour, roast the squash for 40 minutes at 200°C, fan 180°C, gas mark 6, then add to the soup.

BLT with chicken

Why stop at bacon, lettuce and tomato? Add some sliced chicken to make this classic lunchtime sandwich even more delicious.

SERVES 1

PREP TIME
5 minutes

COOK TIME
10 minutes

1 slice Weight Watchers Extra Trimmed Unsmoked Back Bacon
2 slices Weight Watchers Brown Danish Bread
1 teaspoon harissa paste
1 iceberg lettuce leaf

1 small tomato, sliced
70g cooked skinless chicken breast, sliced
Squeeze of lemon juice, to serve
Freshly ground black pepper

1 Put the bacon in a frying pan over a medium heat and cook for 4-5 minutes on each side, or until crisp.

2 Toast the bread, spread with the harissa, then top one slice with the lettuce, tomato, bacon and chicken.

3 Season to taste, drizzle over a little lemon juice, then top with the remaining slice of toast to serve.

IF YOU'RE COUNTING
SmartPoints values per serving 4
SmartPoints values per recipe 4

Top tip...

If you don't like harissa, try spreading the bread with wholegrain mustard or fat-free tomato salsa instead.

Chicken & quinoa curry

A bit like a biryani, but made with quinoa instead of rice, this is a really quick all-in-one dish for curry lovers.

SERVES 4

PREP TIME
15 minutes

COOK TIME
12 minutes

100g quinoa, rinsed and drained
Calorie controlled cooking spray
1 onion, thinly sliced
2 tablespoons mild curry powder
400g cauliflower, cut into small florets
2 courgettes, trimmed and cut into 2cm pieces

125ml chicken stock, made with ½ stock cube
120g frozen peas
500g skinless chicken, cooked and shredded
140g 0% fat natural Greek yogurt
2 tablespoons chopped mint

1   Put the quinoa in a pan with 175ml water. Bring to the boil, then take off the heat, cover and let stand for 12 minutes or until all the liquid is absorbed and the quinoa is fluffy. Drain and set aside.

2   Meanwhile, mist a large, deep frying pan with cooking spray and put over a medium heat. Add the onion and cook, stirring, for 4 minutes until softened. Stir in the curry powder and cook for 1 minute.

3   Add the cauliflower, courgettes and stock. Cover and cook, stirring occasionally, for 6-8 minutes or until the vegetables are tender. Uncover, stir in the peas and cook for 1-2 minutes or until the liquid has evaporated.

4   Stir in the cooked quinoa and chicken, and cook for 1-2 minutes until heated through. Season to taste. Mix the yogurt with the chopped mint and serve with the curry.

IF YOU'RE COUNTING
SmartPoints values per serving 7
SmartPoints values per recipe 26

3 ways with porridge

Simple, convenient and healthy, porridge is brilliant for breakfast.
Make it more interesting with these three easy recipes.

Berry crush porridge

SERVES 1, PREP TIME 5 minutes **COOK TIME** 5 minutes

Microwave 40g **porridge oats** and 250ml water on high for 2½ minutes. Stir, then microwave again for another 1 minute, or until it's at your desired consistency. Meanwhile, in a small bowl, lightly crush 50g **blueberries** and 50g **raspberries** with a fork, then stir through 50g 0% fat natural **Greek yogurt**. Serve the porridge with the berries and yogurt spooned on top.

IF YOU'RE COUNTING
SmartPoints values per serving 5 **SmartPoints** values per recipe 5

Carrot cake porridge

SERVES 1, PREP TIME 5 minutes
COOK TIME 5 minutes

Microwave 40g **porridge oats** and 250ml **skimmed milk** on high for 2½ minutes. Stir, then microwave again for another 1 minute, or until it's at your desired consistency. Stir in 1 small grated **carrot**, and ½ teaspoon **mixed spice**, then serve. For extra sweetness, you could add a small grated pear. You can reduce the SmartPoints values to 4 per serving if you use water instead of skimmed milk.

7 SmartPoints value

IF YOU'RE COUNTING
SmartPoints values per serving 7
SmartPoints values per recipe 7

Apple & spice porridge

SERVES 1, PREP TIME 5 minutes
COOK TIME 5 minutes

Microwave 40g **porridge oats** and 250ml **skimmed milk** on high for 2½ minutes. Stir, then microwave again for another 1 minute, or until it's at your desired consistency. Stir in 1 unpeeled, grated **apple**, ½ teaspoon **cinnamon** and serve. You can reduce the SmartPoints values to 4 per serving if you use water instead of skimmed milk.

7 SmartPoints value

IF YOU'RE COUNTING
SmartPoints values per serving 7
SmartPoints values per recipe 7

Faff-free meals

Plus

3 speedy pasta dishes

Simple but tasty ways with wholemeal pasta for quick lunches or dinners. Page 64

Prawn & apple slaw wraps

These easy wraps pack in plenty of flavour – the apple gives the slaw lots of fruity sweetness while the radishes add a peppery kick.

SERVES 4

PREP TIME
15 minutes

COOK TIME
10 minutes

4 Weight Watchers Tortillas
1 large Granny Smith apple, unpeeled, cored and cut into matchsticks
3 celery sticks, thinly sliced
100g radishes, trimmed and thinly sliced

Handful of fresh mint, shredded, plus extra whole leaves, to serve
100g 0% fat natural Greek yogurt
300g peeled raw prawns
2 teaspoons Cajun seasoning

1 Preheat the oven to 200°C, fan 180°C, gas mark 6. Wrap the tortillas in foil and put on the middle shelf of the oven for 6 minutes.

2 Meanwhile, combine the apple, celery, radishes and shredded mint in a small bowl. Add the 0% fat Greek yogurt. Stir well to combine and set aside.

3 Combine the prawns and the Cajun seasoning in a bowl. Mist a frying pan with cooking spray and heat over a high heat. Cook the prawns for 3 minutes, or until cooked through. Transfer to a plate.

4 Divide the prawns and apple slaw among the tortillas. Add the extra mint leaves, then fold the tortillas in half and serve.

IF YOU'RE COUNTING
SmartPoints values per serving 4
SmartPoints values per recipe 16

Top tip...

Instead of prawns, you could use 400g cooked chicken breast, for a SmartPoints value of 5 per serving.

Steak & black bean salad

This all-in-one salad is a spicy little number – add an extra sprinkling of chilli if you like it hot! Using fresh corn is well worth the effort.

SERVES 4

PREP TIME
15 minutes

COOK TIME
20 minutes

2 corn cobs, husks removed
2 red peppers, deseeded and cut into strips
500g lean rump steak, fat trimmed
Calorie controlled cooking spray
½ teaspoon chilli powder
½ teaspoon ground cumin
½ teaspoon ground coriander

400g tin black beans, rinsed and drained
250g cherry tomatoes, halved
100g watercress
½ red onion, finely sliced
Juice of 1 lime, plus extra lime wedges for serving
Freshly ground black pepper

1   Heat a griddle pan over medium-high heat. Cook the corn cobs for 15 minutes, turning often, until tender and charred. Transfer the corn cobs to a plate and set aside to cool.

2   Add the peppers to the griddle and cook, turning occasionally, until tender and lightly charred. Transfer to a plate and set aside.

3   Mist the steak with cooking spray on both sides. Sprinkle with the spices and cook on the griddle for 2 minutes on each side, or until cooked to your liking. Transfer to a plate, cover and set aside to rest for 5 minutes, then slice into strips.

4   Holding the corn cobs upright, use a small, sharp knife to carefully cut downwards and remove the kernels. Combine the corn kernels, peppers, beans, tomatoes, watercress and onion in a bowl. Squeeze over the lime juice and season to taste. Toss gently to combine and serve topped with the steak and the extra lime wedges on the side.

IF YOU'RE COUNTING
SmartPoints values per serving 7
SmartPoints values per recipe 27

Chargrilled chicken with smoky beans & spinach

Smoked paprika is the secret ingredient that gives this simple dish a distinctive flavour, and makes it just that little bit more special.

SERVES 4

PREP TIME
10 minutes

COOK TIME
20 minutes

Calorie controlled cooking spray
2 garlic cloves, finely chopped
1 red onion, finely chopped
2 teaspoons smoked paprika
300ml chicken stock, made
with ½ chicken stock cube
(ensure gluten free)

400g tin butter beans, drained
400g tin cannellini
beans, drained
50g 0% fat natural Greek yogurt
200g baby leaf spinach
4 skinless chicken breasts
Freshly ground black pepper

1   Mist a deep frying pan with cooking spray and fry the garlic and onion for 5 minutes over a medium heat until softened, but not coloured.

2   Stir in the paprika, then pour in the stock. Simmer for 2 minutes, then add the butter beans and cannellini beans. Leave to simmer for 3-4 minutes until the beans are warmed through. Stir through the yogurt, then add the spinach and stir until just wilted. Season to taste.

3   Meanwhile, lay the chicken breasts on a sheet of cling film and cover with another sheet. Using a rolling pin, beat the chicken until it's about 1.5cm thick. Season well. Mist a griddle pan with cooking spray and cook the chicken over a medium heat for around 5 minutes on each side until cooked through. Remove from the pan and leave to rest for 2 minutes, then slice into thick slices.

4   To serve, divide the bean and spinach stew between 4 shallow serving bowls and top with the sliced chicken breast.

IF YOU'RE COUNTING
SmartPoints values per serving 5
SmartPoints values per recipe 18

Beef & rice stuffed peppers

The whole family will enjoy this dish of red peppers filled with spiced beef and rice. You could make it ahead of time and reheat to serve.

SERVES 4

PREP TIME
20 minutes

COOK TIME
45 minutes

100g brown rice
400g extra lean (5% fat) beef mince
1 small red onion, finely grated
1 teaspoon allspice
1 teaspoon paprika
¼ teaspoon cinnamon
Small handful of fresh dill

Small handful of fresh flat-leaf parsley, chopped
4 large peppers, halved lengthways and deseeded
Calorie controlled cooking spray
1 garlic clove, crushed
500g passata
120g 0% fat natural Greek yogurt

1 Cook the rice according to the pack instructions. Drain, rinse under cold water, then drain again.

2 Preheat the oven to 200°C, fan 180°C, gas mark 6. Combine the cooked rice, beef, onion, allspice, paprika, cinnamon, half the chopped dill and half the parsley in a large bowl. Season to taste.

3 Put the peppers, cut-side up, in a large shallow baking dish. Spoon the beef and rice mixture into the pepper halves. Cover the dish with foil and bake for 15 minutes. Uncover, and continue to bake for 25-30 minutes or until the peppers are just tender.

4 Meanwhile, mist a pan with cooking spray, add the garlic and cook over a medium heat for 1 minute, then add the passata, bring to the boil, then gently simmer for 5 minutes, until slightly reduced. Serve 2 pepper halves per person with the passata sauce drizzled over, topped with a dollop of yogurt and a sprinkling of the remaining dill and parsley.

IF YOU'RE COUNTING
SmartPoints values per serving 5
SmartPoints values per recipe 21

GF **5** SmartPoints value ™

Top tip...
For even more flavour, use smoked paprika to give a wonderfully rich smoky taste.

Chicken & pineapple stir-fry

Stir-frying over a high heat locks in all the flavours in this Oriental-inspired dish and keeps the chicken tender and moist.

SERVES 4

PREP TIME
10 minutes

COOK TIME
25 minutes

200g brown long grain rice
Calorie controlled cooking spray
450g skinless chicken breast, cut into strips
4 spring onions, sliced
1 red pepper, deseeded and cut into bite-size chunks
225g fresh pineapple, chopped

1 red chilli, deseeded and finely chopped
1cm-piece fresh ginger, peeled and grated
¼ teaspoon Chinese five spice powder
2½ tablespoons light soy sauce (ensure gluten free)

1 Cook the rice according to pack instructions. Drain and set aside.

2 Meanwhile, spray a wok or large frying pan with the cooking spray. Heat until very hot, then add the chicken and stir-fry for 5 minutes until well browned, then remove from the pan and set aside. You may need to do this in two batches. Spray the wok again, then add most of the spring onions, pepper and pineapple, and stir-fry for 2-3 minutes.

3 Reduce the heat, add the chilli, ginger and five spice powder, and stir fry for 1-2 minutes. Return the chicken to the pan and add the soy sauce. Stir-fry for 1 minute. Spoon the rice into 4 warmed bowls, top with the stir-fry and garnish with the remaining spring onions to serve.

IF YOU'RE COUNTING
SmartPoints values per serving 6
SmartPoints values per recipe 24

GF

Top tip...

Instead of chicken, you could use 450g lean pork tenderloin for a SmartPoints value of 7 per serving.

Keema curry pies

These spicy individual cottage pies contain plenty of healthy veg, and are topped with a delicious parsnip and cauliflower mash.

SERVES 4

PREP TIME
15 minutes

COOK TIME
50 minutes

300g parsnips, cut into 3cm pieces
400g cauliflower, cut into florets
½ teaspoon turmeric
3 tablespoons chopped fresh coriander
Calorie controlled cooking spray
1 onion, finely chopped
1 carrot, peeled and finely chopped
1 stick celery, finely chopped
3 garlic cloves, crushed
1 tablespoon finely grated fresh ginger
500g extra lean (5% fat) beef mince
1 tablespoon garam masala
1½ teaspoons cumin seeds
400g tin chopped tomatoes
125g frozen peas

1   Cook the parsnips in boiling water for 15–20 minutes or until tender, adding the cauliflower for the last 3 minutes. Drain, return to the pan and heat over low heat for 1 minute to dry out excess moisture, then add the turmeric and coriander, and mash until smooth. Season.

2   Meanwhile, preheat the oven to 200°C, fan 180°C, gas mark 6. Mist a large saucepan with cooking spray and place over medium-high heat. Add the onion, carrot, celery, garlic and ginger, and cook, stirring, for 5–7 minutes or until softened.

3   Add the mince and cook, stirring, for 5 minutes or until browned. Add the garam masala and 1 teaspoon cumin seeds, then cook, stirring, for 1 minute or until fragrant. Add the tomatoes, then fill the empty tin with water and add it to the pan. Simmer gently for 20 minutes or until the beef is tender and the sauce has reduced. Stir in the peas.

4   Spoon the mixture into a 4 individual ovenproof dishes, top with the mash and the remaining cumin seeds. Lightly spray with cooking spray and bake for 30 minutes or until the tops are golden, then serve.

IF YOU'RE COUNTING
SmartPoints values per serving 6
SmartPoints values per recipe 24

Orange & ginger baked salmon

The orange and ginger combines with the soy sauce and vinegar to make a delicious sweet, sour and salty glaze for the fish.

SERVES 4

PREP TIME
15 minutes

COOK TIME
10 minutes

2 oranges, 1½ thinly sliced, juice of the other half
4 x 120g skinless salmon fillets
5cm-piece fresh ginger, cut into matchsticks
2 tablespoons light soy sauce (ensure gluten free)
1 tablespoon rice wine vinegar
1 cauliflower, broken into florets

Calorie controlled cooking spray
Handful of fresh coriander, roughly chopped
2 large pak choi, cut in half lengthways
1 tablespoon soy sauce (ensure gluten free)
2 spring onions, trimmed and sliced into matchsticks

1   Preheat the oven to 220°C, fan 200°C, gas mark 7. Line a baking tray with baking paper. Arrange the orange slices on the baking paper, put the salmon fillets on top and sprinkle the ginger over the salmon.

2   Combine the orange juice, light soy sauce and vinegar in a small jug. Drizzle over the salmon. Bake for 10 minutes or until the salmon is lightly browned and cooked through.

3   Meanwhile, blitz the cauliflower in a food processor until it resembles couscous. Spray a large frying pan with cooking spray and heat over a gentle heat. Stir fry the cauliflower for 3-4 minutes, until cooked but still retaining some bite. Stir through the coriander.

4   Spray another frying pan with cooking spray and stir-fry the pak choi with the soy sauce for 4-5 minutes until wilted.

5   Divide the salmon fillets between 4 serving plates, garnish with the spring onions and serve with the cauliflower and pak choi.

IF YOU'RE COUNTING
SmartPoints values per serving 6
SmartPoints values per recipe 22

GF 6 SmartPoints value

Top tip...
This fabulous dish looks stunning served on a platter so everyone can just dig in.

Greek chicken casserole

Using tinned artichoke hearts is much easier than preparing fresh ones – they add a delicious, nutty flavour to this dish.

SERVES 4

PREP TIME
25 minutes

COOK TIME
30 minutes

Calorie controlled cooking spray
8 plump chicken legs, skinless
1 onion, thinly sliced
1 carrot, peeled and finely chopped
2 garlic cloves, finely chopped
400g tin chopped tomatoes
½ teaspoon dried oregano

½ teaspoon freshly grated nutmeg
400g tin artichoke hearts in brine, rinsed and drained
Small handful fresh flat-leaf parsley, chopped to serve
Freshly ground black pepper

1   Mist a large saucepan with cooking spray and heat over medium-high heat. Season the chicken to taste, then cook it in 2 batches, turning, for 5–7 minutes or until browned. Transfer to a plate.

2   Add the onion, carrot and garlic to the pan and cook, stirring, for 5 minutes or until softened. Return the chicken to the pan, add the tomatoes, oregano and nutmeg, and bring to the boil. Reduce the heat and simmer, covered, for 10 minutes or until the chicken is cooked through.

3   Squeeze any excess liquid from the artichokes and cut in half. Add to the pan and cook for 1–2 minutes or until heated through. Season to taste and serve sprinkled with the chopped parsley.

IF YOU'RE COUNTING

SmartPoints values per serving 9
SmartPoints values per recipe 36

Top tip...

If you can get hold of it, use 2 tablespoons chopped fresh oregano in the casserole, instead of dried.

Chermoula fish parcels

Chermoula – a fragrant, herby salsa – can be used as a marinade for most meat, chicken or fish, or added after cooking as a sauce.

SERVES 4

PREP TIME
25 minutes

COOK TIME
15 minutes

Small handful of fresh coriander leaves
Small handful of fresh flat-leaf parsley leaves
Juice of ½ lemon
1 tablespoon Moroccan spice mix
2 garlic cloves

1 small red chilli, deseeded
4 x 150g firm white fish fillets
1 small lemon, thinly sliced, plus extra wedges to serve
1 red onion, thinly sliced
2 courgettes, thinly sliced
400g tin chickpeas, rinsed and drained

1 Process the coriander, parsley, lemon juice, Moroccan spice mix, garlic and chilli with 2 tablespoons of water in a food processor until almost smooth. Transfer half of the chermoula to a shallow dish, add the fish and turn to coat.

2 Preheat the oven to 220°C, fan 200°C, gas 7. Cut 4 x 30cm squares of kitchen foil and 4 x 30cm squares of baking paper. Put 1 piece of baking paper on top of each piece of foil. Divide the lemon slices, onion, courgettes, chickpeas and fish between the parcels, then fold up the baking paper and foil to enclose everything.

3 Put the parcels on a baking tray and cook for 10-12 minutes or until the fish is just cooked. Unwrap carefully (the steam will be hot) and serve with the extra lemon wedges and remaining chermoula.

IF YOU'RE COUNTING
SmartPoints values per serving 3
SmartPoints values per recipe 12

Italian-style steak & vegetable tagliatelle

The simple ratatouille-style vegetables go so well with steak. Serve this with a side of wholewheat pasta for the full Italian experience.

SERVES 4

PREP TIME
15 minutes

COOK TIME
10 minutes

Calorie controlled cooking spray
1 onion, finely chopped
1 aubergine, diced
2 courgettes, diced
3 tomatoes, diced
2 garlic cloves, crushed

Handful of fresh basil leaves, roughly chopped
200g wholewheat pasta
4 x 120 frying steaks
Small handful of fresh flat-leaf parsley, chopped, to garnish
Freshly ground black pepper

1   Mist a frying pan with cooking spray and heat over a medium-high heat. Add the onion and cook, stirring for 2-3 minutes. Add the aubergine and courgettes, and cook, stirring, for 7-8 minutes. Stir in the tomatoes and garlic, cover and cook over medium heat for 3-5 minutes. Stir in the basil and season to taste, then remove from the heat and set aside.

2   Cook the pasta in boiling water, according to pack instructions, until al dente. Drain and keep warm.

3   Lightly spray a griddle pan with cooking spray and heat over high heat. Season the steaks. Cook for about 2 minutes on each side, depending on how you like them cooked. Serve with the vegetables and pasta, garnished with parsley.

IF YOU'RE COUNTING
SmartPoints values per serving 8
SmartPoints values per recipe 32

Top tip...

Always rest steak on a warmed plate for 3-4 minutes before serving, to give it a much more tender texture.

Turkey with couscous salad

Couscous is a versatile and easy side dish for lots of meals – this recipe uses fresh veg and orange to add plenty of zingy flavour.

SERVES 4

PREP TIME
15 minutes

COOK TIME
10 minutes

Juice and grated zest of 1 orange
2 teaspoons finely chopped fresh rosemary
1 garlic clove, crushed
4 x 100g lean turkey breast steaks
150g mange tout

200g wholewheat couscous
300ml hot chicken stock
Calorie controlled cooking spray
1 cucumber, chopped
60g baby spinach
150g radishes, trimmed and finely sliced
Freshly ground black pepper

1 Combine half the orange juice with the rosemary and garlic in a dish. Add the turkey and turn to coat. Put in the fridge for 10 minutes.

2 Put the mange tout in a bowl, pour over enough boiling water to cover them and let them stand for 2 minutes. Meanwhile, fill a bowl with cold water and add some ice cubes. Drain the mange tout and put them in the bowl of iced water for 1 minute. Drain, pat dry, then slice in half on the diagonal.

3 Put the couscous in a bowl. Pour over the hot stock, cover and leave for 10 minutes until all the stock has been absorbed. Fluff up the grains with a fork and set aside.

4 Preheat a frying pan over a medium-high heat. Remove the turkey from the marinade, drain and mist with cooking spray. Cook for 3 minutes on each side. Transfer to a plate, cover and set aside.

5 Add the orange zest, mange tout, cucumber, spinach, radishes and remaining orange juice to the couscous. Season and mix gently to combine. Slice the turkey steaks and serve with the salad.

IF YOU'RE COUNTING
SmartPoints values per serving 7
SmartPoints values per recipe 26

Roast turkey pilaf

This is a great all-in-one dish for family dinners. Roasting the sprouts before adding them to the pilaf really intensifies their flavour.

SERVES 4

PREP TIME
25 minutes

COOK TIME
30 minutes

350g Brussels sprouts, trimmed and halved
Calorie controlled cooking spray
1 large onion, finely chopped
2 celery sticks, finely chopped
2 garlic cloves, crushed
4 cardamom pods
1 cinnamon stick
1 teaspoon cumin seeds
200g brown rice

1 litre hot chicken stock, made with 1 stock cube (ensure gluten free)
200g skinless roast turkey breast, chopped
2 tablespoons chopped fresh coriander leaves, plus extra to garnish
½ teaspoon dried chilli flakes
Freshly ground black pepper

1   Preheat the oven to 200°C, fan 180°C, gas mark 6. Put the sprouts in a roasting tray, mist with cooking spray, season well and roast in the oven for around 20 minutes, or until soft.

2   Meanwhile, mist a large pan with cooking spray and add the onion and celery. Cook, stirring regularly, for 5 minutes or until the vegetables start to soften. Add the garlic and cook, stirring, for a further 2 minutes.

3   Add the spices and season. Cook, stirring, for 1 minute, then stir in the rice and chicken stock. Bring to the boil, then reduce the heat, cover and simmer for 25 minutes, removing the lid after 20 minutes.

4   Add the turkey and sprouts, and cook for a further 2 minutes, uncovered, until the rice is tender and the turkey is warmed through. Stir in the coriander, and season to taste, then served sprinkled with the dried chilli flakes and with the extra coriander.

IF YOU'RE COUNTING
SmartPoints values per serving 6
SmartPoints values per recipe 25

Griddled pork with freekeh & nectarine salad

Freekeh is made from young wheat grains that are roasted to give them an earthy, nutty flavour. Try it in this simple salad recipe.

SERVES 4

PREP TIME
15 minutes

COOK TIME
25 minutes

150g roasted wholegrain freekeh
2 small cucumbers, chopped
Large handful of fresh mint leaves, shredded
1 red onion, finely chopped
Calorie controlled cooking spray

4 firm nectarines, cut into thick wedges
4 x 100g lean pork loin steaks, fat trimmed
Freshly ground black pepper

1 Cook the freekeh according to the pack instructions. Cool slightly, then put in a large bowl with the cucumbers, mint and onion. Season and toss to combine.

2 Mist a griddle pan with cooking spray and preheat over a medium-high heat. Put the nectarine slices on the griddle and cook, turning occasionally for 4-5 minutes or until golden and tender. Transfer to a plate. Cover loosely with foil to keep warm.

3 Season the pork to taste. Spray the griddle pan with a little more cooking spray and cook the pork for 2-3 minutes on each side, or until cooked though. Serve the salad topped with the pork and griddled nectarines.

IF YOU'RE COUNTING
SmartPoints values per serving 10
SmartPoints values per recipe 38

Top tip...

You could also cook the pork on a barbecue, preheated to medium, for 2-3 minutes on each side.

3 speedy pasta dishes

Wholewheat pasta is an incredibly versatile (and great tasting) starting point for all kinds of meals. Try these quick and simple ideas…

Tagliatelle with pork & mushrooms

SERVES 4, PREP TIME 15 minutes **COOK TIME** 20 minutes

Mist a large, deep frying pan with **calorie controlled cooking spray**. Add 1 sliced **onion** and cook for 3-4 minutes over a medium heat, then add 400g thinly sliced **lean pork steaks**, season well and cook for 5-6 minutes. Reduce the heat and stir in 4 crushed **garlic cloves**. Add 250g sliced **button mushrooms** and cook for 5 minutes.

Stir in 2 tablespoons **chopped parsley**, 100g **fat-free fromage frais** and 100ml **vegetable stock**. Cook for 7-8 minutes until thickened. Meanwhile, cook 250g **wholewheat tagliatelle** according to pack instructions. Drain well, stir in 260g **baby spinach** and let it wilt, then serve with the pork and mushrooms, sprinkled with a little **paprika**.

IF YOU'RE COUNTING
SmartPoints values per serving 10 **SmartPoints** values per recipe 40

Roasted butternut & red onion penne

SERVES 2, PREP TIME 10 minutes
COOK TIME 40 minutes

Preheat the oven to 200°C, fan 180°C, gas mark 6. Toss 500g peeled, cubed **butternut squash** with 1 teaspoon **paprika** and ½ teaspoon **chilli flakes** in a roasting tin, and mist with **calorie controlled cooking spray**. Roast for 40 minutes, adding 1 **red onion**, cut into wedges, for the last 15 minutes. Transfer to a bowl, pour in 100ml **vegetable stock** and lightly mash with a fork. Meanwhile, cook 150g **wholewheat penne** according to pack instructions. Drain, reserving some of the cooking water. Toss the squash mixture with the pasta, and about 6 tablespoons of the cooking water. Sprinkle over 1 tablespoon chopped **fresh sage**, then serve.

 IF YOU'RE COUNTING
SmartPoints values per serving 7
SmartPoints values per recipe 14

Spaghetti with smoked trout & lemon

SERVES 4, PREP TIME 5 minutes
COOK TIME 10 minutes

Bring a large saucepan of water to the boil and cook 375g **wholewheat spaghetti** according to pack instructions, or until just tender. Add 2 bunches of trimmed and sliced **asparagus** and 120g frozen **peas** for the final 2 minutes of cooking time. Drain the pasta and vegetables, and return to the pan. Add 200g **hot-smoked trout** torn into chunks, 2 teaspoons grated **lemon zest** and 1½ tablespoons **lemon juice**. Season to taste and toss to combine, then serve.

IF YOU'RE COUNTING
SmartPoints values per serving 11
SmartPoints values per recipe 45

No Count veggie

Plus

3 easy buckwheat risottos

Using buckwheat instead of rice makes a tasty change – and is quicker, too. Page 84

Warm aubergine & pomegranate salad

Fresh mint and parsley play a starring role in this delicious warm salad that includes lots of fragrant Middle Eastern flavours.

SERVES 4

PREP TIME
10 minutes

COOK TIME
20 minutes

3 large aubergines, trimmed and cut into 1cm-thick slices
Calorie controlled cooking spray
1 tablespoon Moroccan spice mix
2 x 67g Weight Watchers Wholemeal Pitta Pockets
Large handful of fresh flat-leaf parsley leaves

Small handful of fresh mint leaves
3 tablespoons pomegranate seeds
2 tablespoons balsamic vinegar
Grated zest and juice of ½ lemon
Freshly ground black pepper

1 Pre-heat the grill to medium. Heat a griddle pan over medium-high heat. Put the aubergine slices in a bowl. Spray with the oil and sprinkle with the spice mix. Season and toss to combine. Cook the aubergine on the griddle, in batches, for 4-5 minutes on each side or until tender.

2 While the aubergine cooks, lightly spray the pitta breads with cooking spray and cook under the grill for 2 minutes on each side until lightly toasted. Allow to cool slightly, then break into large pieces.

3 Arrange the aubergine, pitta, parsley and mint on a large serving platter. Sprinkle with the pomegranate seeds.

4 In a small jug, whisk the balsamic vinegar with the lemon juice and zest. Season, then drizzle over the salad and serve immediately.

IF YOU'RE COUNTING
SmartPoints values per serving 3
SmartPoints values per recipe 10

Stuffed courgettes

These are served with a tomato side salad for a colourful Mediterranean-style main course that has plenty of fresh flavour.

SERVES 4

PREP TIME
20 minutes

COOK TIME
35 minutes

5 courgettes
Calorie controlled cooking spray
250g reduced-fat cottage cheese
Grated zest of 1 lemon
¼ teaspoon dried chilli flakes
Handful of fresh basil leaves, chopped
Handful of fresh mint leaves, chopped

400g mixed baby tomatoes, halved
½ red onion, thinly sliced
1 tablespoon balsamic vinegar
70g rocket
Freshly ground black pepper

1   Preheat the oven to 180°C, fan 160°C, gas mark 4. Line a large baking tray with baking paper. Halve 4 of the courgettes lengthways. Using a teaspoon, remove most of the flesh from the courgette halves, leaving a 1cm border around the edges. Discard the flesh and mist the outside of the courgette shells with cooking spray. Put the courgette shells on the prepared baking tray, skin side down.

2   Coarsely grate the remaining courgette and put it into a bowl. Mix in the cottage cheese, lemon zest, chilli flakes and ¾ of both the basil and mint. Season.

3   Divide the mixture evenly among the courgette shells. Bake for 30–35 minutes or until the courgettes are tender and the filling is golden.

4   Combine the tomatoes, onion, vinegar, rocket and remaining basil and mint in a large bowl. Serve with the courgettes.

IF YOU'RE COUNTING
SmartPoints values per serving 1
SmartPoints values per recipe 5

Quinoa & roasted veg salad

Roasting the vegetables for the salad really intensifies their flavour.
If you can't find tricolour quinoa, just use the regular variety.

SERVES 4

PREP TIME
30 minutes

COOK TIME
1 hour 35
minutes

2 small beetroot, scrubbed
300g sweet potato, peeled and
cut into 2cm chunks,
1 red onion, cut into
thin wedges
Calorie controlled cooking spray
300g broccoli, cut into florets

200g tricolour quinoa, rinsed
500ml vegetable stock, made
with 1 stock cube
Juice of 1 lemon
Large handful of fresh flat-leaf
parsley leaves, chopped
Freshly ground black pepper

1   Pre-heat the oven to 180°C, fan 160°C, gas mark 4. Put the beetroot
    on a large sheet of foil and wrap to enclose. Bake for 1 hour or until
    tender. When cool enough to handle, peel the beetroot and cut into
    thin wedges.

2   While the beetroot is cooling, line a large baking tray with baking paper.
    Spread the sweet potato and onion on the tray and mist with cooking
    spray. Bake for 20 minutes. Mist the broccoli with cooking spray, add
    to the tray and bake for a further 15 minutes or until tender.

3   Meanwhile, put the quinoa and stock in a saucepan over high heat.
    Bring to the boil. Reduce heat and simmer, covered, for 15-20 minutes
    or until the liquid is absorbed and the quinoa is tender and translucent.
    Transfer to a bowl and leave to cool for 5 minutes.

4   Combine the quinoa with the beetroot, sweet potato, onion and broccoli
    in a large bowl. Add the lemon juice and season. Add the parsley and
    gently toss to combine, then serve.

IF YOU'RE COUNTING
SmartPoints values per serving 7
SmartPoints values per recipe 29

Chilli chickpea pasta

Chickpeas and pasta may seem like an odd combination, but they work really well together. The garlic, lemon and chilli add a zesty kick.

SERVES 4

PREP TIME
10 minutes

COOK TIME
10 minutes

250g wholewheat fusilli pasta
Calorie controlled cooking spray
1 red onion, finely chopped
2 garlic cloves, crushed
Grated zest and juice of
½ lemon
1 red chilli, deseeded and
finely chopped

400g tin chickpeas, rinsed
and drained
400g Tenderstem broccoli,
trimmed
100ml vegetable stock, made
with ½ stock cube
100g rocket
Freshly ground black pepper

1   Cook the pasta in a saucepan of boiling water according to the pack instructions. Drain, then return to the pan.

2   Meanwhile, mist a large non-stick frying pan with cooking spray and put over a medium heat. Add the onion and cook, stirring, for 5 minutes or until softened. Add the garlic, lemon zest and chilli and cook, stirring, for 30 seconds or until fragrant. Add the chickpeas, broccoli and stock. Bring to the boil then reduce the heat, cover and cook for 2 minutes or until the broccoli is just tender.

3   Add the chickpea mixture, rocket and lemon juice to the pasta in the pan. Season to taste, toss to combine and serve.

IF YOU'RE COUNTING
SmartPoints values per serving 8
SmartPoints values per recipe 30

Asparagus & basil omelette

Omelettes are brilliant for a speedy lunch for one – this one is flavoured with basil, then topped with asparagus and cottage cheese.

SERVES 1

PREP TIME
2 minutes

COOK TIME
10 minutes

2 asparagus spears, chopped
Calorie controlled cooking spray
2 eggs
1 tablespoon chopped,
fresh basil

5 teaspoons reduced-fat
cottage cheese
1 x 35g slice Weight Watchers
Brown Danish Bread
Freshly ground black pepper

1   Microwave the asparagus on high for about 30 seconds until just tender. Drain if necessary. Preheat the grill to medium.

2   Mist a small frying pan with cooking spray and put over a medium heat. Beat the eggs with the basil and 1 tablespoon of water, and season. Pour the eggs into the pan, swirl around and tip the pan from side to side to allow any uncooked egg to run over the edges of the cooked egg. Continue to cook until just slightly wet on top.

3   Top the omelette with the asparagus and dollop on the cottage cheese. Put the pan under the grill and cook for 2-3 minutes until the top of the omelette is just set. Sprinkle over some black pepper and serve with the bread.

IF YOU'RE COUNTING
SmartPoints values per serving 6
SmartPoints values per recipe 6

Top tip...

Try mange tout instead of asparagus – about 100g should be fine. Steam in the microwave for 30 seconds before adding.

Aubergine, spinach & lentil stacks

An impressive looking veggie dish that's great for entertaining.
It takes a little longer to make, but is well worth the effort.

SERVES 4

PREP TIME
30 minutes

COOK TIME
40 minutes

200g dried Puy lentils
3 large aubergines, sliced
lengthways into 12 slices
Calorie controlled cooking spray
1 red onion, finely chopped
2 garlic cloves, crushed
400g mixed baby tomatoes,
halved

Small handful of fresh basil,
shredded
180g quark
50g young leaf spinach
1½ tablespoons balsamic
vinegar
Freshly ground black pepper

1   Cook the lentils in a large saucepan of boiling water, according
    to pack instructions, until just tender. Drain and set aside.

2   Meanwhile, heat a griddle pan over a hight heat. Mist the aubergine
    with cooking spray and cook in batches on the griddle for 4-5 minutes
    on each side, or until tender, then set aside.

3   Mist a frying pan with cooking spray. Add the onion and garlic, and
    cook over a medium heat, stirring, for 5 minutes. Add the tomatoes
    and cook, stirring, for 5 minutes or until they start to soften. Stir in the
    lentils and heat through, then add the basil. Season to taste.

4   Put 3 aubergine slices on each of 4 serving plates. Layer them together
    with the lentil and tomato mixture, the quark and the spinach leaves
    – reserve a few spinach leaves to garnish. Drizzle over the balsamic
    vinegar and serve.

IF YOU'RE COUNTING
SmartPoints value per serving 5
SmartPoints values per recipe 20

Quinoa burger pittas

Fancy a burger? Try these ones made from sweet potato and quinoa, served in pittas with tender roasted vegetables.

SERVES 4

PREP TIME
30 minutes

COOK TIME
1 hour 10 minutes

2 courgettes, sliced lengthways
1 red pepper, deseeded and cut into strips
250g cherry tomatoes, halved
Calorie controlled cooking spray
250g sweet potato, peeled and roughly chopped
50g tricolour quinoa
1 small garlic clove, crushed

½ red onion, finely chopped, the other half finely sliced
2 teaspoons balsamic vinegar
4 x Weight Watchers Wholemeal Pitta Breads
70g rocket
1 tablespoon chopped, fresh flat-leaf parsley

1 Pre-heat the oven to 200°C, fan 180°C, gas mark 6. Put the courgettes, pepper and tomatoes on a baking tray lined with baking paper, mist with cooking spray and roast for 25 minutes until tender. Transfer to a plate and set aside to cool. Keep your oven on.

2 Meanwhile, cook the sweet potato in a pan of boiling water for 15 minutes or until tender. Drain and mash in a bowl. Cook the quinoa according to pack instructions, then drain and add to the sweet potato.

3 Mist a frying pan with cooking spray and put over a medium heat. Add the garlic and chopped onion and cook, stirring, for 2 minutes. Add to the quinoa and sweet potato. Season and mix well. Shape the mixture into 4 patties, put on the baking tray and mist with cooking spray. Cook in the oven for 40-45 minutes until golden, turning halfway. Once cooked, leave for 5 minutes before handling as they will be fragile.

4 Combine the roasted vegetables with the balsamic vinegar and season. Warm the pittas in the oven for 2 minutes, then fill each one with a burger, roasted veg, rocket, sliced red onion and parsley, and serve.

IF YOU'RE COUNTING
SmartPoints values per serving 7
SmartPoints values per recipe 26

Chickpea vegetable curry

This recipe is great for family mealtimes and freezes well, so you could make a double batch and save half for another time.

SERVES 4

PREP TIME
10 minutes

COOK TIME
25 minutes

200g brown rice
Calorie controlled cooking spray
1 onion, chopped
1 aubergine, cut into chunks
4 garlic cloves, chopped
1 teaspoon cumin seeds, lightly crushed
6 cardamom pods
5 cloves
Large pinch crushed chilli

1 teaspoon black onion seeds
1 teaspoon turmeric
400g tin chickpeas, drained
250ml vegetable stock, made with ½ stock cube (ensure gluten free)
3 tomatoes, chopped
100g young leaf spinach
75g 0% fat natural Greek yogurt

1 Cook the rice according to pack instructions. Drain and set aside.

2 Mist a large nonstick frying pan with cooking spray and add the onion and aubergine. Cook gently, stirring occasionally, for 6-7 minutes or until softened. Add the garlic, cumin, cardamom, cloves, chilli and onion seeds, and cook for 2 minutes, stirring all the time.

3 Stir in the turmeric and cook for 1 minute, then add the chickpeas, stock and tomatoes. Bring to the boil and simmer for 5 minutes over a medium-high heat. Add the spinach and cook for 1 minute or until wilted. Season to taste. Serve in warmed shallow bowls with the yogurt and rice.

IF YOU'RE COUNTING
SmartPoints values per serving 7
SmartPoints values per recipe 27

Top tip...

Take care when cooking the spices as they can burn easily. If you need to, add a splash of water to cool things down.

3 easy buckwheat risottos

Risotto is a great all-in-one dish that you can flavour in lots of different ways. These quick and easy versions use buckwheat, instead of rice.

Fennel & lemon risotto

SERVES 4, PREP TIME 15 minutes **COOK TIME** 25 minutes

Pre-heat the oven to 200°C, fan 180°C, gas mark 6. Cut 2 **fennel bulbs** into quarters and cut out the core. Put on a baking tray, mist with **calorie controlled cooking spray** and season. Roast for 20-25 minutes. Allow to cool slightly, then slice half the fennel thinly, and set the rest aside. Meanwhile, mist a heavy-based saucepan with cooking spray and cook 1 sliced **onion** for 5 minutes until softened. Add 1 crushed **garlic**

clove, cook for 1 minute, then add 250g **buckwheat** and the sliced fennel. Add 750ml **vegetable stock** (ensure gluten free) stirring regularly until all the liquid is absorbed and the buckwheat is tender – about 12-14 minutes. Stir in the **juice of half a lemon** and 100g **quark**. Top with the remaining fennel quarters and sprinkle over 2 tablespoons chopped flatleaf parsley and 1 tablespoon grated **lemon zest** to serve.

 IF YOU'RE COUNTING
SmartPoints values per serving 6 **SmartPoints** values per recipe 25

Mixed mushroom & thyme risotto

SERVES 4, PREP TIME 10 minutes
COOK TIME 20 minutes

Mist a heavy-based saucepan with **calorie controlled cooking spray** and cook 1 thinly sliced **leek** and 1 crushed **garlic clove** for 5 minutes. Add 250g **buckwheat**, 1 teaspoon **fresh thyme** leaves and 750ml hot **vegetable stock** (ensure gluten free) stirring regularly until all the liquid is absorbed and the buckwheat is tender – about 12-14 minutes. Meanwhile, mist a non-stick frying pan with cooking spray and cook 400g chopped mixed **mushrooms** until softened. Stir the mushrooms into the risotto for the last 5 minutes of cooking time. Serve topped with 150g **reduced-fat cottage cheese** and **60g rocket**.

7 **IF YOU'RE COUNTING**
SmartPoints values per serving 7
SmartPoints values per recipe 28

Roasted cherry tomato risotto

SERVES 4, PREP TIME 10 minutes
COOK TIME 15 minutes

Pre-heat the oven to 200°C, fan 180°C, gas mark 6. Mist 600g **cherry tomatoes** with **calorie controlled cooking spray**, drizzle over 2 teaspoons **balsamic vinegar** and season. Put on a baking tray and roast for 8-10 minutes. Meanwhile, mist a heavy based saucepan with cooking spray and cook 1 chopped **onion** for 5 minutes. Add 1 crushed **garlic clove**, cook for 1 minute, then add 250g **buckwheat**. Add 750ml hot **vegetable stock** (ensure gluten free), stirring regularly until all the liquid is absorbed and the buckwheat is tender – about 12-14 minutes. Stir in the tomatoes and 3 tablespoons chopped **basil** to serve.

7 **IF YOU'RE COUNTING**
SmartPoints value per serving 7
SmartPoints a per recipe 26

Easy entertaining

Plus

3 stuffings for turkey

Transform a plain turkey breast joint with these flavour-packed fillings. Page 106

Asian pork salad cups

These are inspired by *san choy bao*, a popular dish in south-east Asia. Think of them as fragrant, spicy pork wraps – in lettuce leaves!

SERVES 6

PREP TIME
15 minutes

COOK TIME
10 minutes

100g 100% buckwheat soba noodles (we used Clearspring)
Calorie controlled cooking spray
400g extra lean (5% fat) pork mince
1 lemon grass stick, tough outer leaves removed, finely chopped
2cm-piece fresh ginger, peeled and grated
4 fresh kaffir lime leaves, finely shredded

100g beansprouts
1 carrot, peeled and cut into matchsticks
Large handful of fresh mint leaves, shredded
3 tablespoons soy sauce (ensure gluten free)
Juice of 1 lime
12 baby gem lettuce leaves, washed and patted dry
4 spring onions, finely shredded
Freshly ground black pepper

1   Cook the noodles according to pack instructions, then rinse under cold water in a colander, drain and chop them into short lengths. Set aside.

2   Mist a wok with cooking spray and put over a high heat. When the wok is very hot, add the pork and stir fry for 5 minutes or until browned and cooked through.

3   Add the lemon grass, ginger and half the lime leaves, and stir-fry for 2 minutes. Remove from the heat. Add the beansprouts, carrot, mint, soy sauce, lime juice and noodles, and toss to combine. Season with pepper.

4   Arrange the lettuce leaf 'cups' on serving plates. Spoon in the pork mixture, sprinkle over the remaining lime leaves and the spring onions, then serve immediately.

Top tip...

Instead of noodles, you could cook 150g brown rice to pack instructions and use that for the same SmartPoints values.

IF YOU'RE COUNTING

SmartPoints values per serving 4
SmartPoints values per recipe 22

Scallops with mango salsa

These make a delicious (and super easy) starter and are also great as canapés with drinks. Take care not to overcook the scallops.

SERVES 6

PREP TIME
10 minutes

COOK TIME
2-3 minutes

½ small red pepper, deseeded and finely diced

½ ripe mango, peeled and finely chopped

1 tablespoon finely chopped fresh coriander

1 tablespoon finely chopped fresh chives

Juice of ½ lime, plus extra lime wedges to serve

Calorie controlled cooking spray

12 scallops (without roe)

1   Put all the ingredients except the scallops in a small bowl, mix well, then divide the salsa between 12 Chinese-style soup spoons.

2   Mist a griddle pan with cooking spray and preheat over a high heat. Cook the scallops for 1 minute on each side, or until cooked and golden, and season.

3   Put a scallop on top of the salsa in each of the spoons, then serve.

IF YOU'RE COUNTING
SmartPoints values per serving 0
SmartPoints values per recipe 1

Top tip...

You could also serve the salsa in small lettuce leaf cups, topped with the scallops (see p88).

Mini pea & mint frittatas

These tasty morsels are so easy to make and are the perfect finger food for a party. Make plenty, as they're sure to disappear fast.

MAKES 24

PREP TIME
10 minutes

COOK TIME
12 minutes

Calorie controlled cooking spray
6 eggs
50ml skimmed milk
90g frozen peas
2 shallots, finely chopped

50g reduced-fat natural cottage cheese
2 tablespoons chopped fresh mint, plus extra to serve

1 Preheat the oven to 200°C, fan 180°C, gas 4. Mist two 12-hole mini muffin trays with cooking spray.

2 In a large jug, beat together the eggs with the milk, then season. Put the peas in a heatproof bowl and pour boiling water over them to cover. Leave for 1 minute, then drain, run under cold water and drain well. Add to the egg mixture, along with the shallots, cottage cheese and mint. Stir to combine, then divide the mixture between the muffin trays and bake for 12 minutes or until just set. Serve warm, sprinkled with the extra chopped mint.

IF YOU'RE COUNTING
SmartPoints values per serving 1
SmartPoints values per recipe 15

Top tip...

The family will love these little fritattas and they are fantastic with a fresh green salad for a tasty packed lunch.

Griddled seafood platter

Wow your guests with this simple-but-impressive platter of prawns, scallops and fish skewers, with a herb and yogurt dipping sauce

SERVES 8

PREP TIME
15 minutes

COOK TIME
15 minutes

350g skinless, boneless salmon fillets
350g skinless, boneless firm white fish, such as cod
1 lemon
300g raw king prawns, tails on
8 scallops
Calorie controlled cooking spray
½ teaspoon dried chilli flakes

FOR THE HERBY YOGURT DIP
300g low-fat natural yogurt
2 tablespoons finely chopped fresh dill
2 tablespoons chopped fresh chives
Juice of ½ lemon, plus extra lemon and lime wedges to serve

1 Combine the ingredients for the herby yogurt dip, season and set aside.

2 Cut the salmon and white fish into 24 cubes each. Cut the lemon into quarters, then thinly slice crossways. Thread the cubed fish and lemon slices onto 8 skewers. Put the prawns and scallops on a plate and mist with cooking spray, then sprinkle over the chilli flakes.

3 To cook the fish skewers, heat a large griddle pan over a high heat. Mist the skewers with cooking spray and season. Cook for 2-3 minutes on each side until golden and cooked through. Set aside and keep warm while you cook the remaining seafood.

4 Put the prawns and scallops on the griddle and cook for 1-2 minutes on each side, then arrange them on a platter with the fish skewers and serve with the herby yogurt dip and lemon and lime wedges.

IF YOU'RE COUNTING
SmartPoints values per serving 3
SmartPoints values per recipe 22

Top tip...

No griddle pan? Cook the fish under a hot grill (soak the skewers first), and the prawns and scallops in a frying pan.

Pork & fennel meatballs

Fancy a plate of Italian-style perfection? Fennel-flavoured meatballs are simmered in a spicy tomato sauce and served with courgetti.

SERVES 4

PREP TIME
10 minutes,
plus chilling

COOK TIME
50 minutes

500g extra-lean (5% fat) pork mince
1 tablespoon fennel seeds
Grated zest of ½ lemon
1 egg, lightly beaten
Calorie controlled cooking spray
1 red onion, finely chopped
2 garlic cloves, finely chopped

1 red chilli, deseeded and finely chopped
2 x 400g tins chopped tomatoes
1 tablespoon balsamic vinegar
3 large courgettes, spiralised
1 tablespoon chopped fresh flat-leaf parsley
Freshly ground black pepper

1   For the meatballs, mix the pork with the fennel seeds, lemon zest and the egg to bind. Season, then shape into 12 equal balls. Chill in the fridge for 30 minutes to firm up.

2   Mist a large pan with cooking spray, add the onion, garlic and most of the chilli, and cook over a low heat for 10 minutes until soft. Add the tomatoes and balsamic vinegar, and simmer over a low heat for 30 minutes until the sauce is thickened and sticky. Season to taste.

3   Mist a large non-stick frying pan with the cooking spray, add the meatballs and fry over a medium-high heat for 8-10 minutes, turning often, until they are cooked through and browned on all sides. You may need to do this in batches. Add the cooked meatballs to the pan of spicy sauce and simmer together for another couple of minutes.

4   Cook the courgetti in a pan of boiling water for 3-4 minutes or until tender, drain and divide between bowls. Top with the meatballs and sauce, and garnish with the rest of the chilli and the parsley, to serve.

IF YOU'RE COUNTING
SmartPoints values per serving 5
SmartPoints values per recipe 18

GF · 5 SmartPoints value™

Orange & chilli chicken drumsticks

This impressive-looking dish is bursting with zingy, spicy flavour.
The griddled vegetables make an unusual side to go with it.

SERVES 4

PREP TIME
20 minutes,
plus
marinating

COOK TIME
50 minutes

8 chicken drumsticks, skinless
Grated zest and juice
of 1 orange
1 red chilli, deseeded
and chopped
2 teaspoons finely chopped
thyme leaves, plus extra to serve
1 tablespoon smoked paprika

1 tablespoon ground cumin
2 garlic cloves, crushed
400g new potatoes
Calorie controlled cooking spray
200g asparagus
2 baby cos lettuce, cut in
half lengthways
1 lemon, cut into 4 wedges

1   In a large bowl, combine the chicken, orange zest and juice, chilli, thyme, paprika, cumin and garlic. Cover and put in the fridge to marinate for 30 minutes.

2   Put the potatoes in a saucepan and cover with cold water, then bring to the boil over a medium heat. Cook for 10-15 minutes until just tender, then run under cold water to cool. Drain, cut in half lengthways and set aside. Bring another pan of water to the boil and cook the asparagus for 1-2 minutes or until just tender. Drain and transfer to a bowl of iced water until cold, then remove and put on a paper towel to drain.

3   Preheat the oven to 200°C, fan 180°C, gas mark 6. Put the chicken on a large baking tray with all the marinade, season and roast for 40 minutes, turning halfway through.

4   About 15 minutes before the chicken has finished cooking, heat a griddle pan and mist with cooking spray. Griddle the potatoes on both sides until golden. Repeat with the asparagus and lettuce. Serve the veg with the chicken, the extra fresh thyme and lemon wedges.

IF YOU'RE COUNTING
SmartPoints values per serving 7
SmartPoints values per recipe 26

Beef fillet with chimichurri

This modern take on roast beef is served with succulent roasted tomatoes and chimichurri – a zingy, spicy, herb and garlic salsa.

SERVES 8

PREP TIME
20 minutes

COOK TIME
40 minutes,
plus resting

1.2kg lean beef fillet,
fat trimmed
Calorie controlled cooking spray
400g cherry tomatoes on
the vine
Large handful of fresh flat-leaf
parsley, leaves chopped

Large handful of fresh coriander,
leaves chopped
2 garlic cloves, crushed
1 teaspoon dried chilli flakes
1 tablespoon red wine vinegar
Juice of ½ lemon

1 Take the beef out of the fridge 20 minutes before cooking. Preheat the oven to 180°C, fan 160°, gas 4.

2 Pat the beef dry with paper kitchen towels. Mist a large frying pan with cooking spray and put it over a high heat. When the pan is hot, add the beef and sear, turning until it is browned all over. Transfer to a roasting tin and cook in the oven for 35-40 minutes, depending on how you like it cooked. Add the vine tomatoes to the roasting tin for the last 15 minutes of cooking time.

3 Meanwhile, make the chimichurri: combine all the remaining ingredients in a bowl with 2 tablespoons water and season to taste.

4 Once the beef is cooked, remove it from the oven, transfer to a plate and cover with foil. Leave to rest for 15 minutes, then carve and serve with the roasted tomatoes and chimichurri.

IF YOU'RE COUNTING
SmartPoints values per serving 4
SmartPoints values per recipe 35

Top tip...

Adjust the amount of chilli in this fiery salsa, adding only a couple of pinches if you prefer just a hint of heat.

Courgette-wrapped fish

This is so simple to put together, but looks really special. Serve with vegetables of your choice, such as boiled new potatoes and peas.

SERVES 4

PREP TIME
15 minutes

COOK TIME
15 minutes

2 large courgettes
4 x 150g firm white fish fillets,
such as haddock or cod

FOR THE LEMON & HERB SAUCE
175g quark
2 tablespoons vegetable stock
(ensure gluten free)

Juice of ½ lemon, plus
extra lemon wedges, to serve
1 tablespoon chopped
fresh chives, plus extra to serve
1 tablespoon chopped fresh dill,
plus extra to serve

1 Line the base of a plastic or hob steamer with baking paper. Put 3-4cm of water in the bottom pot of the steamer and bring to a simmer.

2 Using a vegetable peeler, slice the courgettes into wide ribbons. Put a quarter of the courgette ribbons on a chopping board and lay out, slightly overlapping each other, so they're wide enough to encase the fish fillets. Put a fillet on the courgette ribbons and wrap them to completely cover the fish. Put the parcel into the lined steamer and repeat with the remaining courgette ribbons and fish fillets.

3 Steam the fish for 8-10 minutes, or until it has turned opaque and the courgette is just softened.

4 Meanwhile, make the sauce. Put the quark in a small saucepan over a low heat and stir until melted. Stir in the stock, then remove from the heat and stir through the lemon juice, chives and dill. Season to taste. Serve the fish parcels with the sauce drizzled over, sprinkled with the extra herbs, with lemon wedges on the side.

IF YOU'RE COUNTING
SmartPoints values per serving 1
SmartPoints values per recipe 2

Top tip...

Take care when heating the quark for the sauce – too much heat can make this ultra low-fat soft cheese split.

Paella with chicken

A Spanish classic, all-in-one paella is perfect for entertaining.
This version uses only chicken, but you could also add seafood.

SERVES 8

PREP TIME
10 minutes

COOK TIME
50 minutes

900ml chicken stock (ensure gluten free)
½ teaspoon saffron
Calorie controlled cooking spray
400g skinless chicken breast, cut into 2cm pieces
1 onion, diced
1 large red pepper, deseeded and diced

2 garlic cloves, crushed
300g brown rice
3 teaspoons smoked paprika
400g tin chopped tomatoes
120g frozen peas
Handful of fresh flat-leaf parsley, chopped
Lemon wedges, to serve

1   Put the stock and saffron in a large saucepan over a high heat and bring to the boil. Remove from the heat, cover and keep warm.

2   Heat a large, deep, nonstick frying pan over a medium-high heat and mist with cooking spray. Add the chicken and stir fry for 3-4 minutes until just browned, then transfer to a plate.

3   Reduce the heat and mist the pan with cooking spray again. Add the onion, red pepper and garlic, and cook, stirring, for 3 minutes until they are softened, then add the rice and paprika. Stir and cook for 1 minute, then add the tomatoes and half the stock. Bring to a simmer, season to taste and cook for 20 minutes, stirring occasionally.

4   After 20 minutes, add the chicken, peas and half of the remaining stock. Cook for a further 10 minutes, adding more of the remaining stock if it seems too dry. Test to check that it's cooked. Once cooked, stir through the parsley and serve the paella with lemon wedges.

IF YOU'RE COUNTING
SmartPoints values per serving 5
SmartPoints values per recipe 39

3 stuffings for turkey

Want something special for entertaining guests? Transform a turkey breast joint with one of these three mouthwatering fillings.

Turkey with apple & sage stuffing

SERVES 8, PREP TIME 20 minutes **COOK TIME** 1 hour 15 minutes, plus resting

Put 1 peeled, chopped **Bramley apple** in a pan with a splash of water over a medium heat, and cook for 10 minutes. Meanwhile, mist a frying pan with **calorie controlled cooking spray** and cook 4 chopped Weight Watchers Extra Trimmed Unsmoked Back **Bacon Medallions** over a medium heat for 5 minutes. Add 1 finely chopped **onion** and cook for a further 5 minutes. Put the apple, bacon and onion in a bowl and combine with 200g **breadcrumbs** made from Weight Watchers Brown Danish Bread, 6 finely chopped **sage** leaves and 1 beaten **egg**. Preheat the oven to 180°C, fan 160°C, gas mark 4. Make a slit along the side of a 1.2kg skinless, boneless **turkey breast** and fill with the stuffing mixture. Tie with kitchen string and mist with cooking spray. Season and roast for 1 hour 15 minutes. Leave to rest for 15-20 minutes before carving.

IF YOU'RE COUNTING
SmartPoints values per serving 4 **SmartPoints** values per recipe 29

Turkey with mushroom & quark stuffing

SERVES 8, PREP TIME 25 minutes
COOK TIME 1 hour 15 minutes, plus resting

Mist a pan with **calorie controlled cooking spray** and cook 1 chopped **onion** over a medium heat for 10 minutes or until softened. Add 2 crushed **garlic cloves** and 250g chopped **chestnut mushrooms**, and cook for 5 minutes. Transfer to a bowl and allow the mixture to cool, then add 250g **quark**, 100g **breadcrumbs** made from Weight Watchers Brown Danish Bread, 1 tablespoon chopped fresh **thyme**, 1 tablespoon chopped fresh **rosemary** and 1 beaten **egg** and mix well. Season, then use to stuff and cook a 1.2kg **turkey breast**, as with the apple and sage stuffing recipe.

 IF YOU'RE COUNTING
SmartPoints values per serving 3
SmartPoints values per recipe 23

Turkey with quinoa & bacon stuffing

SERVES 8, PREP TIME 25 minutes
COOK TIME 1 hour 15 minutes, plus resting

Cook 100g **quinoa** in boiling water for 15 minutes. Drain and set aside to cool. Mist a pan with **calorie controlled cooking spray**, add 4 chopped Weight Watchers Extra Trimmed Unsmoked Back **Bacon Medallions** and cook over a medium heat for 5 minutes. Add 1 chopped **onion**, cook for 5 minutes, then add 2 crushed **garlic cloves** and cook for 1 minute. In a bowl, combine the quinoa with the bacon and onion mixture, then add the juice and zest of 1 **orange**, 2 teaspoons chopped fresh **rosemary** and 1 beaten **egg**. Season, then use to stuff and cook a 1.2kg **turkey breast**, as with the apple and sage stuffing recipe.

 IF YOU'RE COUNTING
SmartPoints values per serving 3
SmartPoints values per recipe 26

Snacks & puds

Plus

3 No count dippers
Simple snacks that are bursting
with flavour. Page 116

3 frozen desserts
Perfect warm-weather
puds the easy way. Page 126

Spicy roasted chickpeas

These spicy little snacks made from tinned chickpeas
are so moreish – make them as hot, or not, as you like.

SERVES 4

PREP TIME
5 minutes

COOK TIME
45 minutes

400g tin chickpeas, drained and rinsed
1 teaspoon ground cumin
1 teaspoon smoked paprika
Pinch of cayenne pepper
Calorie controlled cooking spray
Freshly ground black pepper

1   Preheat the oven to 180°C, fan 160°C, gas mark 4. Pat the
chickpeas dry with kitchen paper and spread them out on a small
baking tray. Sprinkle over the cumin, paprika and cayenne pepper,
and mist with the cooking spray. Season, then toss so the chickpeas
are all well coated with the spices.

2   Roast for 45 minutes, turning halfway through cooking. Serve warm.

IF YOU'RE COUNTING
SmartPoints values per serving 2
SmartPoints values per recipe 7

Top tip...

You could make double
the quantity, then cool
and store in an airtight
container for up
to a week.

Red pepper dip

This colourful dip tastes as good as it looks and makes a great snack, or starter for an alfresco summer meal.

SERVES 4

PREP TIME
20 minutes

COOK TIME
15 minutes

4 red peppers
Calorie controlled cooking spray
1 small red onion, chopped
1 garlic clove, sliced
1 teaspoon fresh thyme leaves
Juice of ½ a lemon

2 teaspoons balsamic vinegar
Cayenne pepper, to taste
Crudités and ½ quantity spiced tacos, to serve (see p116)

1. Using a pair of kitchen tongs, put the whole peppers over the flame on a gas cooker, or under a hot grill, and slowly turn until blackened all over. Put in a heatproof bowl and cover with cling film. Set aside to cool for 20 minutes.

2. While the peppers are cooling, mist a small pan with cooking spray and put over a low-medium heat. Add the onion and cook for 10 minutes or until softened. Add the garlic and thyme, and cook for 1 minute, then set aside to cool.

3. Peel the skin off the cooled peppers. Cut the peppers in half and discard the seeds, then roughly chop the flesh and put in a food processor with the onion and herb mixture, the lemon juice, balsamic vinegar and cayenne pepper. Process until fairly smooth, then serve with the crudités and tacos.

IF YOU'RE COUNTING
SmartPoints values per serving 1
SmartPoints values per recipe 4

Top tip...
If you'd like the dip to have a smokier flavour, use a good pinch of smoked paprika instead of the cayenne pepper.

Carrot & chickpea dip

This chunkier variation of a classic houmous is full of flavour from the carrot, herbs and spices. Lemon juice adds a citrussy zing.

SERVES 4

PREP TIME
15 minutes

COOK TIME
15 minutes

1 large carrot, peeled and chopped
Calorie controlled cooking spray
1cm-piece fresh ginger, peeled and grated
2 garlic cloves, crushed
1 teaspoon ground cumin

1 teaspoon ground coriander
400g tin chickpeas, drained and rinsed
3 tablespoons low-fat natural yogurt
2 teaspoons lemon juice
Crudités, to serve (see p117)

1 Bring a small pan of water to the boil, add the carrot and cook for 6-8 minutes or until soft. Drain and set aside.

2 Mist a pan with cooking spray, put over a medium heat, add the ginger and garlic and cook for 2 minutes, then add the cumin and coriander. Cook for 1 minute, then add the cooked carrot. Stir to combine then set aside to cool.

3 Put the chickpeas in a food processor with the cooled carrot mixture, the yogurt and lemon juice. Season and process until fairly smooth, adding a splash of water if the mixture is too thick. Serve the dip with the crudités.

IF YOU'RE COUNTING
SmartPoints values per serving 3
SmartPoints values per recipe 10

Top tip...
Try swapping the carrot for 200g cooked beetroot, and the ginger and spices for 1 teaspoon grated horseradish.

3 No Count dippers

Get ready to dunk! Dips make brilliant healthy snacks and are also great for parties. Serve them up with these easy dippers.

Spiced tacos

SERVES 6, PREP TIME 5 minutes **COOK TIME** 7 minutes

Preheat the oven to 200°C, fan 180°C, gas mark 6. Tear 2 **Weight Watchers Wraps** into bite-size pieces, spread over a nonstick baking sheet and mist with **calorie controlled cooking spray**. Sprinkle with **smoked paprika** and **chilli powder** to taste, and season well. Using your fingers, turn the pieces of wrap to coat them in the spices. Bake for 5 minutes, then turn over and bake for another 2 minutes until golden and crisp. Serve straight away.

 IF YOU'RE COUNTING
SmartPoints values per serving 1 **SmartPoints** values per recipe 6

VIP veggie crudités

SERVES 6, PREP TIME 10 minutes **GF** **V**

Seek out colourful and unusual veg to make your crudités platter special. We've used **baby carrots**, **asparagus**, **watermelon radishes**, **celeriac** sticks and **mini cucumbers** – about 400g in total. Buy them as fresh as possible so they're nice and crisp. Rinse well, then trim, peel and cut larger veg into fingers. Arrange them on a platter and garnish with sprigs of fresh herbs. Serve alongside your favourite dip, or try mixing 150g 0% fat natural Greek yogurt (if you're counting, that's 2 SmartPoints) with chopped fresh herbs, seasoning and a squeeze of lemon juice for a really quick and tasty option.

IF YOU'RE COUNTING
SmartPoints values per serving 0 (without yogurt).
SmartPoints values per recipe 0 (without yogurt)

Herby potato wedges

SERVES 6, PREP TIME 5 minutes
COOK TIME 30 minutes **GF** **V**

Preheat the oven to 200°C, fan 180°C, gas mark 6. Pierce 1 large **potato** (200g) and one large **sweet potato** (200g) with a sharp knife, then put on a microwave-safe plate and microwave on high for 8 minutes until they are just starting to feel tender. When cool enough to handle, cut into wedges and put on a large nonstick baking sheet. Mist with **calorie controlled cooking spray** and season with **pepper** and **garlic salt**, then roast for 10 minutes. Add 2 sprigs of fresh **rosemary** and roast for another 10 minutes until golden. Serve warm.

IF YOU'RE COUNTING
SmartPoints values per serving 2
SmartPoints values per recipe 11

Jewelled citrus salad with lime & mint

This fruit salad on a platter looks so pretty – you can mix and match the fruit depending on what is in season at the time.

SERVES 6

PREP TIME
10 minutes

2 ruby grapefruit
2 large oranges
2 clementines or satsumas
12 physalis berries
Seeds of ½ pomegranate

Zest of 1 lime
1 tablespoon chopped, fresh mint leaves
1 tablespoon artificial sweetener

1   Peel the grapefruit, oranges and clementines, removing as much of the white pith as you can. For the grapefruit and oranges, you may find it easier to use a knife to slice the top and bottom off, then cut away the rest of the peel. Slice the fruit crossways, removing any seeds.

2   Arrange the slices of fruit on a platter. Reserve 4 of the physalis berries intact, then remove the others from their papery pods, cut the berries into halves and scatter them over the other fruit. Scatter over the pomegranate seeds.

3   Using a pestle and mortar, crush the lime zest, mint leaves and artificial sweetener together until you have a rough paste. Add 1-2 tablespoons of water, mixing, until you have a drizzling consistency. Garnish the fruit salad with the reserved physalis berries and serve with the lime and mint dressing to drizzle over.

IF YOU'RE COUNTING
SmartPoints values per serving 0
SmartPoints values per recipe 0

Baked apples with forest fruits & frozen yogurt

The combination of the soft, warm apples and berries with the cold frozen yogurt makes this fruity dessert irresistible.

SERVES 4

PREP TIME
20 minutes,
plus freezing

COOK TIME
45 minutes

200g low-fat natural yogurt
2 tablespoons artificial sweetener
1 vanilla pod
250g frozen black forest fruits
Pinch of ground mixed spice
4 apples, such as Braeburns, cored

1 First, make the frozen yogurt. Put the yogurt and sweetener in a small bowl. Cut the vanilla pod in half lengthways, scrape out the seeds from one half and stir them into the yogurt. Transfer to a freezer-proof container, cover and freeze for at least 3 hours or overnight.

2 Preheat the oven to 180°C, fan 160°C, gas mark 4. Put the frozen fruits in a small pan with the mixed spice and the other half of the vanilla pod. Heat gently, stirring occasionally, until the fruit begins to soften.

3 Sit the cored apples in a small baking dish, just big enough to hold them. Fill the holes with some of the forest fruits, then spoon the rest into the dish around the apples. Bake for 40 minutes or until the apples are soft.

4 Remove the frozen yogurt from the freezer about 15 minutes before serving to allow it to soften, and serve with the apples and forest fruits.

IF YOU'RE COUNTING
SmartPoints values per serving 1
SmartPoints values per recipe 5

Griddled peaches

These luscious peaches are served still warm with a citrus cream – velvety smooth quark flavoured with vanilla and orange.

SERVES 4

PREP TIME
5 minutes

COOK TIME
6 minutes

150g quark
3 teaspoons Truvia
Seeds from ¼ vanilla pod
Zest and juice of ½ an orange
6 just-ripe peaches, halved and de-stoned
Seeds of 1 pomegranate

1. To make the citrus cream, combine the quark, Truvia, vanilla seeds and orange zest and juice. Set aside and chill until needed.

2. Preheat a griddle pan over a medium-high heat. Add the peaches, cut side down, and cook for 3 minutes on each side until softened and lightly charred.

3. Divide the warm peaches among 4 serving bowls and scatter with the pomegranate seeds. Serve with a spoonful of the citrus cream.

IF YOU'RE COUNTING
SmartPoints values per serving 1
SmartPoints values per recipe 3

Top tip...
If you haven't used Truvia before, it's a plant-based calorie-free sweetener that's much sweeter than sugar, so use sparingly.

Clementine jelly creams

This is a great get-ahead dessert – you can make the jelly a day in advance, then top with the vanilla cream just before serving.

SERVES 4

PREP TIME
25 minutes,
plus infusing
and chilling

COOK TIME
5 minutes

5 clementines
2 fruit tea bags
1 sachet sugar-free orange
jelly granules
150g quark
1 teaspoon artificial sweetener
1 teaspoon vanilla extract

1 Carefully grate the zest from one of the clementines, then peel and segment all of them, making sure to remove all pith, and divide the segments among 4 serving glasses.

2 In a saucepan, bring 285ml water to the boil with the tea bags, cover and leave to infuse for 1 hour until cool, then remove the tea bags.

3 Empty the contents of the jelly sachet into a bowl and add another 285ml just-boiled water, stirring until the jelly is completely dissolved. Stir the cooled fruit tea into the jelly. Pour the jelly mixture over the clementines in the serving glasses, then put in the fridge for 3-4 hours, or until completely set.

4 Once the jelly is set, make the cream. Put the quark, sweetener and vanilla extract in a small bowl and mix gently until smooth. Divide the cream equally among the glasses, spooning it over the jellies. Sprinkle over the clementine zest, then serve.

IF YOU'RE COUNTING
SmartPoints values per serving 1
SmartPoints values per recipe 2

3 frozen desserts

For the perfect summery pud, serve a scoop of one of these mouthwatering frozen fruity treats that everyone will love.

So-simple banana 'ice cream'

SERVES 4, PREP TIME 5 minutes, plus freezing

Put 5 ripe **bananas**, 4 tablespoons **skimmed milk** and the seeds from ½ **vanilla pod** in a food processor and process until smooth. Pour the mixture into a freezer-proof container, cover and freeze for 2 hours. Remove from the freezer, break up with a fork and stir well. Return to the freezer and repeat the freezing and stirring process twice more. Serve in scoops or, if you're entertaining, try pressing softened ice cream into small bowls, then refreeze until firm, turn out onto a plate and serve with fresh **blackberries** and **passion fruit** pulp.

 IF YOU'RE COUNTING
SmartPoints values per serving 0 **SmartPoints** values per recipe 1

Frozen raspberry yogurt

SERVES 4
PREP TIME 10 minutes, plus freezing

Put 400g frozen **raspberries**, 500g 0% fat natural **Greek yogurt**, 1 teaspoon **artificial sweetener** and a pinch of **dried mint** into a food processor, and pulse until combined. Tip the mixture into a freezer-proof container and fold in 150g **fresh raspberries**. Cover and freeze for 1 hour, then remove from the freezer, break up with a fork and stir well. Return to the freezer and repeat the freezing and stirring process twice more, then leave to freeze until firm. If the yogurt becomes too solid, leave out of the freezer for 5-10 minutes to soften before scooping.

 IF YOU'RE COUNTING
SmartPoints values per serving 2
SmartPoints values per recipe 6

Mango & lime sorbet

SERVES 8
PREP TIME 10 minutes, plus freezing time

Peel, de-stone and roughly chop 6 ripe **mangos** and put the flesh (about 600g) in a food processor. Add the zest and juice of 1 **lime** and 2 teaspoons **Truvia**. Whiz to a smooth purée, then pour into a freezer-proof container. Cover and freeze for 2 hours, then remove from the freezer, break up with a fork and stir well. Repeat the freezing and stirring process twice more, until the sorbet has a smooth consistency. Return to the freezer until firm, then serve in scoops. This is delicious on its own or served with fresh blueberries.

 IF YOU'RE COUNTING
SmartPoints values per serving 0
SmartPoints values per recipe 0

Recipe index

SmartPoints index